C000143556

# Beyond Stress
## Growing into serenity

## Jennifer Minney

with illustrations by
**Brian Minney**

*Silvertree Publishing*

Published 2001
by
Silvertree Publishing
PO Box 2768, Yeovil, Somerset

ISBN: 0-9538446-4-1

Printed and bound by
Bookcraft, Midsomer Norton

# Author's Note

For the sake of clarity, the masculine pronoun "he" has been used throughout the book, although the text is equally, and in some cases more, applicable to women.

# Contents

# 1

## INTRODUCTION AND OVERVIEW

### A STRESSFUL SOCIETY

#### Stress and Rapid Change

Stress is not primarily a feeling, but a physical response to external pressure or threat, whether real or imagined. It is a complex set of biochemical changes that prepares the body for immediate action: either fight or flight. The action may involve dealing with a natural stressor, such as a bacterial invasion, or coping with a threatening person or dangerous situation. The biochemical reaction is meant to be short-lived. But, in this rapidly changing, high-tech age, we are constantly exposed to the anxiety-provoking conditions that induce fight or flight. So, we are chronically stressed.

In addition to those physical stressors that our ancestors experienced, such as pain, hunger, heat or cold, and threats of emotional or bodily harm, we are also constantly bombarded with frightening images through news programmes, horror movies and the like. And every day we hear or read about political tension, racial unrest, natural disasters, epidemics, the threat of nuclear accidents.... So we walk around carrying permanent mental images of violence or impending disaster. The anxiety they create activates the fight or flight reaction just as if we were ourselves in danger.

The acceleration of change during the last century has also resulted in information overload. We are constantly having to assimilate new knowledge and adjust to new thoughts, ideas and ways of living — again leading to stress. And the current emphasis on academic skills, with the associated devaluing of manual dexterity, means that we have greater pressure to do well at school, pass exams, and go on to further education. These demands are especially stressful for people who are not academically inclined. In addition, we are subjected, as never before, to contact overload. This is partly because of the population explosion, but also because of the shift from rural to urban living. The result is overcrowding, with people literally living on top of each other, and increased violence and crime. In cities especially, people live with a high level of alertness to danger.

During the last century, we also became more mobile. We travel far more than our ancestors did, and at far greater speeds. This, of course, has its advantages. But the combination of burgeoning cities and expanding businesses has made commuting a necessity for many, and the daily stress of getting to and from work can be one pressure too many — especially if the job itself is stressful. Not only is there traffic congestion to contend with, but road works, noise, petrol fumes and other drivers who may be slow, unpredictable, irate or even dangerous. With train or bus travel there is the stress of being crammed with other people into small spaces, and anxiety about delays and meeting connections. And with air travel there is the additional strain of jet lag. Improved transport may have enabled us to visit and enjoy places that our forebears could only dream about, but at the cost of our health, not least because, in spite of all our dashing around, we are actually less fit.

### Stress and Sedentary Living

The twentieth century shift from manual labour to work based on information exchange means that, in addition to our having more mental pressures than people of previous generations, we have also become more sedentary. We therefore have insufficient exercise, so our bodies become less supple and lack stamina, and there is a greater risk of obesity. Being sedentary makes us more susceptible to disease, such as hypertension or heart failure; more prone to colds and flu; and less able to cope with the normal stresses and strains of life.

Sedentary living is associated with the change from being largely self-supporting to being interdependent. We depend on others to provide food, clothes, furniture and household goods that our forebears generally made themselves – with the

exception of the very rich. So, we have become lazy. And the abundance of microwave meals, boil-in-the-bag meals, and pre-packaged, ready-to-eat snacks has created in us a tendency to overeat. As with improved transport, the availability of such a wide range of foodstuffs from so many different countries is a source of enrichment. But, in addition to its harmful effect with regard to physical fitness, we are also more vulnerable to food scares, like E coli, BSE or salmonella. We are constantly having to make choices about risk factors, and often without the necessary information to do so. This creates a feeling of helplessness, of not being in control, which is very frightening and therefore very stressful.

Our dependency on others is increased by the proliferation of labour saving devices – vacuum cleaners, washing machines, dishwashers, etc. These have certainly made life easier, but again more sedentary, the extra time usually being devoted to mental work or passive play. For example, the prevalence of TV, videos and the internet means that, having spent all day sitting behind a wheel, then at a desk or in front of a computer screen, many people then spend the evenings slumped in front of the TV. The inventions of the last century have not only increased our susceptibility to stress by making us more sedentary, but also by making us more materialistic.

## Stress and Materialism

Paradoxically, although we are less active than people of previous generations, we have lost the ability to rest: to be still and allow our bodies and minds to relax. Instead we succumb to materialism, which is the tendency to prefer material possessions and physical comfort to spiritual values. This in turn makes us more susceptible to time stress, despite the technical advances that have taken the drudgery out of so many kinds of work. The pressures of the age have also led us to take on increasingly more work in order to buy bigger houses, better cars, or more advanced equipment, and to fill our wardrobes with designer clothes and our children's cupboards with the trendiest toys. There may be times when we stop and question, when we wonder just what life is all about. But not for long. The pull of materialism is very strong.

People who are spiritually inclined, who are deeply aware of the need for time and space in order to develop the soul – that part of the self that is concerned with life, emotions and creative thought — are not immune from the effects of materialism. Churches are full of people who are dashing around from one meeting to another, involved in numerous committees, being pulled in different directions by a diversity of needs. They are driven, not so much by the urge to make more money or get on in life, but with the equally materialistic need to show something tangible for their efforts; something that can be reckoned up and quantified. This is because people are no longer valued simply for what they are, and because it is no longer considered a good use of time to just sit and reflect on the beauty and wonder of creation. We have to be up and doing. And there is constant pressure to keep up with changing thoughts and trends. If we fail, there is a very real danger that we will be considered to have passed our sell-by date. And we will be cast aside.

## Stress and Impermanence

The materialistic ethos that developed in the last century is particularly exemplified by our throw-away mentality. Everything comes packaged, so everyone has become used to discarding masses of unwanted plastic and cardboard. And nothing is made to last. So, instead of repairing torn clothes or broken furniture, we simply get rid of them and buy new. This creates a sense of impermanence, which gives rise to anxiety, leading to the fight or flight reaction. The generalised feeling of uncertainty is exacerbated by the knowledge that nowadays there is no such thing as a job for life. Instead, there is the constant threat of take-overs and redundancy, and a continual search for more desirable jobs with better prospects, more pay and greater spin-offs. This means that there is also a greater propensity to keep uprooting and moving house. Even if we stay put, neighbours come and go, village shops and schools close down, new houses are built.... Nothing stays the same, not even those established beliefs and values that, until the latter half of the twentieth century, provided a solid foundation on which to build our lives.

The sense of impermanence is revealed through an erosion of those Judaeo-Christian values that have stood firm for millennia. For instance, marriage, that was once considered sacred and expected to be "until death us do part", is questioned and even held in contempt. The firm disciplining of children has been outlawed, so parents are losing control and becoming increasingly anxious in consequence. And victims of criminal activity can no longer rely on there being justice or expect to find safety in laws that protect the innocent. The basic tenets of Christianity themselves are being eroded in the name of care and sensitivity. Christians are no longer thrown to the lions for their biblical beliefs and ethics; instead, they are told that they are discriminatory and made to feel guilty, confused and anxious. It is no wonder that we are more prone to stress than any previous generation.

Since we are living in a particularly stressful society, and everyone is susceptible to the pressures of the age, it is important that you become alert to its dangers, noting how *you* become overly stressed and ensuring that you do not allow yourself to succumb to this potentially fatal condition. This means, first of all, understanding just what stress is, and learning to recognise what happens in your body when the fight or flight reaction is activated.

# WHAT IS STRESS?

## Acute Stress

People talk about feeling stressed, but stress itself, as has been noted, is not primarily a feeling but a complex set of physical reactions to external pressure or threat, whether existing in reality or in the imagination. The stressors — the factors that lead to stress — are related to negative emotions, especially fear and grief, and are connected with change. The change of relationship or circumstances may not be unwelcome, but actively sought for: marriage, a new baby, promotion, career change, a house move.... But whether it is negative or positive, the reactions, which are meant to be for crisis conditions only, are the same. The response to negative change is referred to as distress. This is the stress of losing. The response to positive change has been termed eustress. This is the stress of winning.

When there is any kind of pressure or threat, the chain of biochemical reactions is triggered by the sympathetic nervous system, a branch of the automatic nervous system that supplies involuntary muscles and glands. This acts on a part of the brain called the hypothalamus, which stimulates the pituitary gland at the base of the brain to produce a hormone called ACTH. This, in turn, stimulates the adrenal glands, located just above the kidneys, to produce a variety of hormones, including adrenalin. The circulating adrenalin causes certain blood vessels to constrict, diverting blood supply away from the extremities and internal organs, where it is not needed, towards the brain and major muscle groups.

At the same time, there is a surge of energy, supplied by extra glucose released from the liver; and an increase in oxygen, due to the heart beating more rapidly and intensively. To further aid the readiness for fight or flight, the number of circulating lymphocytes (used to fight infection) is reduced, and blood-clotting agents increased. Also, hearing becomes more acute and vision more sensitive. In other words, everything that is not needed in the crisis is temporarily shut down, while those parts of the body needed to combat danger, or run from it, are put into a state of high arousal.

## Chronic Stress

When there is exposure to unrelieved pressure or threat, the body remains in a constant state of arousal. So, because of the constricted blood vessels and the strain placed on the heart, there is increased risk of arteriosclerosis, hypertension, stroke and heart disease. The persistent increased blood supply to the brain and major muscle groups results in headaches and muscle tension, with associated aches and pains, especially of the neck. The poor circulation to the extremities means that there is more sensitivity to cold; and the reduced blood supply to the stomach and other internal organs, with increased acidity and slowing down of digestive processes, leads to a variety of digestive disorders, including stomach and duodenal ulcers and kidney damage. The decreased number of circulating lymphocytes means that injuries heal more slowly and the body becomes more vulnerable to infection and disease, including cancer; while the increased blood-clotting rate leaves a person susceptible to thrombosis and other circulatory diseases. The acute hearing leaves one less able to cope with noise, and the ultra-sensitive vision can result in eye damage. Chronic stress ultimately leads to complete physical breakdown — and death.

If you are now suspecting that any physical difficulties you might have are stress related, then you can further increase your awareness by deciding if you are particularly at risk. The more you can recognise your vulnerability to stress, the better able you will be to develop some form of protection.

## WHO IS MOST LIKELY TO BECOME STRESSED?

### Men

No one is immune from stress. It can strike anyone, regardless of age, gender, nationality or religion. But some people are more prone than others. Especially at risk are men, who are far more susceptible to stress-related illnesses than women. This is possibly because of the dominant role that, until recently, men have been expected to play in the workplace. Men have traditionally been more exposed than women to business pressure, deadlines, conflict and hostility. Even today, in spite of equality, men are expected to be the strong ones, able to protect and provide for their families, to lead and be the cornerstones of society. The effort to live up to the tough "John Wayne" image can take a great toll, especially as men are stereotypically not supposed to show, or even have, feelings. The inability to be in touch with one's emotional side and safely give vent to feelings creates a tremendous build-up of pressure. It also results in a lack of balance − essential for stress management − making a person unable to respond to the more gentle, cooperative part of himself, and more likely to be ruled by hard-headed logic.

Since the rise of feminism in the seventies, the reverse might also be true. Nowadays, men are often pulled in different directions, feeling that they are expected to nurture their softer side at the expense of their natural more aggressive tendencies. This too is highly stressful because it creates a need to fight or run from an essential part of one's being.

**Competitive People**

People of either gender who are very competitive high-flyers, people who don't let emotions get in the way of success, are also more prone to stress. Sometimes described as "Type A" personalities, these people have a strong need to achieve, and they tend to be workaholics, finding it difficult to relax and have fun. They generally have unhealthy lifestyles — poor eating habits, smoking, lack of exercise — and they are more susceptible to time pressure, setting themselves deadlines as they try to accomplish more and more in progressively less time. And they do not tolerate obstacles and setbacks. Their drive to succeed is not entirely due to innate factors. Such people are likely to have experienced inordinate pressure from their parents while growing up, and learned from them this potentially destructive behaviour.

**Damaged People**

People who have been damaged in childhood, through abuse or neglect, rejection or constant criticism, are more prone to emotional disturbances in later life, such as depression or stress.

This is partly because of the erosion of self-esteem that results from not being unconditionally loved and accepted. Their poor sense of self and lack of confidence makes them more fearful of failure, disapproval or loss, whether it is loss of family, job, money or status. So for them, minor setbacks or disagreements can be overwhelming. Being hurt in childhood also creates a high anger level which makes it more difficult to cope with minor irritations, and a propensity to feel guilty, even when they are not at fault. The constant self-blame leads to a drive to perfectionism; while the underlying fear that comes from being mistreated makes them want to avoid conflict or confrontation. So, they are repeatedly stressed by the same people or situations. In addition, damaged people, especially those who have been constantly put down, being told that they will never amount to anything, tend to gravitate towards jobs that are highly-demanding, but without the coping skills necessary to meet those demands. As a result, they expose themselves to yet more stress.

## People in High-Pressure Jobs

People in certain kinds of jobs, even if they generally cope well with stress, are particularly at risk because of the nature of their work. One group consists of those who have direct contact with demanding or irate customers, teachers, and professional carers: doctors, nurses, social workers, psychiatrists, counsellors and the like. Much of their stress comes from contact overload: being constantly exposed to people who are emotionally and physically draining. Those responsible for others' mental well-being are especially at risk as they tend to take their patients' problems home with them. Another group comprises people who are responsible for the safety of others, especially if this requires unrelieved, intense concentration. Most notoriously at risk are air-traffic controllers. A third group is made up of workers with hazardous jobs, such as bomb disposal experts, and those who have to handle dangerous tools, animals or people. A fourth group includes employees in monotonous jobs, like factory workers, whose industry is machine-paced. This creates feelings of helplessness and lack of control, as well as boredom. Being under-stimulated can be as stressful as having too much pressure.

If you are in a high-stress job, or are susceptible to stress because of your gender, personality type, upbringing or the demands of society, you need to be particularly alert to the presence of stress. You might find it helpful to make a note of those factors that most identify you as being at risk. And as well as getting to know yourself more, and your areas of vulnerability, you need to be able to recognise the typical signs and symptoms of stress. Signs are what show on the outside and can be seen by others; symptoms are what you feel inside.

## SIGNS AND SYMPTOMS OF STRESS

### Emotional Signs and Symptoms

People experience stress in different ways, depending on their general make-up and areas of weakness. But the most common emotional symptoms are feelings of not coping, of being overwhelmed by the quantity and complexity of tasks to be accomplished, especially if there is a deadline to meet. Stress is often associated with negative thinking — about oneself or others — boredom and apathy, an inability to make decisions, lack of concentration, chronic anxiety, and a tendency to mood swings or bouts of depression. There is likely also to be a low tolerance to frustration, with feelings of irritability at others' seeming slowness or incompetence, a liability to over-react to mental pressure or physical stimuli, and difficulty unwinding. Untreated stress can lead to recognised psychological disorders, such as panic attacks and obsessive-compulsive behaviour. But whatever the emotional effects of stress, it always reveals itself also in physical signs and symptoms.

**Physical Signs and Symptoms**

Stress tends to home in on the weakest point in the body. So, for instance, if you have a back injury, stress will tend to result in backache. The most common symptoms are muscular tenseness, shakiness, or feeling physically overstretched, like a rubber band that is about to snap. Chronic fatigue, lack of energy, breathlessness and a sense of being weighed down are also typical symptoms of stress, as are unexplained headaches, neck pain, sweaty palms or a proneness to "pins and needles", nausea, diarrhoea, and a frequent need to urinate. The signs include tremor, especially of the hands, a general twitchiness, a tendency to be "on edge" and snap at the slightest provocation or jump on hearing sudden loud noises. Facial tics are also common, and a propensity to flush or break out in a rash.

Unrelieved stress can give rise to psychosomatic symptoms; that is, physical illnesses that have a psychological cause. Although the cause is emotional, the illnesses are real, not imagined, so they do require medical intervention. These include cardiovascular disease, especially high blood pressure, kidney failure, liver disease, digestive disorders, and some types of cancer. Chronic stress also leads to a reduction of sex hormones: testosterone in men and progesterone in women, which results in reduced sex drive and, in women, menstrual irregularities. Because stress interferes with the immune system, there is likely to be an increased vulnerability to illnesses and less ability to deal with the normal pressures of living. The physical, as well as the emotional, effects of stress inevitably bring about changes in behaviour that interfere with the formation of healthy relationships and with general functioning.

## Behavioural Signs and Symptoms

Stress often shows itself in dysfunctional ways of relating to others: with impatience, irritability or overt aggression. Or it may be manifested in unpredictability, so that family and friends don't know what to expect from one day to the next. There are often disturbed sleep patterns, with accident proneness, decreased appetite or sex drive, and a habit of bursting into tears, often for no apparent reason. There may be a predisposition to drive oneself to achieve higher grades, complete more tasks, or earn more money, while knowing that these gains are not essential. On the other hand, there may be an inclination to give up, leaving behind a trail of broken promises and half-finished tasks. Frequently, people cope with chronic stress by binge eating or turning to alcohol or drugs, such as sleeping pills. In severe cases, it can lead to reclusive, antisocial or even criminal behaviour. If stress levels become unbearable, there may be an escape into insanity or suicide.

Since people experience stress in different ways, it is important that you recognise your own set of typical signs and symptoms, especially in the early stages, so that you can learn how to deal with stress before it becomes overwhelming. It is also essential that you discover the types of stressors that are most likely to affect you. The causes of stress are many and complex, consisting not only of current pressures or threats, but of past, unresolved conflicts that make people more prone to stress in the first place. Therefore, before you can move forward, growing out of stress into serenity, you have to go back. You have to look into your own childhood in order to discover the root causes of stress, and how you may be repeating the patterns of childhood and actually stressing yourself.

# 2

## THE CAUSES OF STRESS

### CURRENT FACTORS

#### Types of Stressors

Stressors, the factors that activate the biochemical stress reaction, are usually associated with change. And since change is often sought for and welcomed, it follows that the effort needed to establish a new relationship, or cope with a different set of circumstances or new thoughts and ideas, may actually be enjoyable. A certain amount of stress is also healthy. Just as muscles need the right amount of tension to keep us upright and functioning, so also the soul needs some emotional tension to provide challenge and stimulation, and to enhance performance. For example, feeling a bit anxious and nervous before making a public speech can improve delivery, whereas too much fear will get in the way, causing the speaker to forget major points, stumble over words, and generally come across as hesitant and unsure of himself.

Nowadays, stress is more often a hindrance than a help, because there is usually too much of it. Therefore, whether the stressors come from external sources or from inside oneself, and whether they cause distress or eustress, it is essential that one learns to recognise them. Only then can unnecessary stress be avoided. For easier identification, we will divide the stressors into four main groups, according to their origins: situational factors, people, time, and one's own thoughts and expectations. However, these are not four distinct kinds of stressor; one leads to another, and they merge and overlap.

While identifying the kinds of stressor to which you are most vulnerable, it is important that you also recognise the stressors that you enjoy, like, for instance, the buzz of skydiving or the mental stimulation that comes from studying. It takes practice to develop an awareness of stress and the specific ways it affects your own mind and body. But, in time, you will have a better idea of the kinds of stressor you should most avoid, and the kinds you should, in moderation, embrace.

### Situational Stress

Stress is classed as situational when it arises from circumstances that are potentially harmful, or that are perceived to be frightening or beyond one's ability to control. The most distressing event one can experience is the death of a spouse. Whether or not the relationship was a happy one, death brings about change, so the stress reaction is the same — although feelings of grief and depression will vary. Also high up on the list are divorce or separation, or the death of a family member or close friend. Others include sexual difficulties, or being involved in quarrels with family or neighbours. Anything that damages or curtails relationships is always stressful.

Among the more prevalent situational stressors is work overload, which leads to feelings of helplessness, futility and anxiety. The same applies for financial difficulties, being arrested or made redundant. Situations that have an important bearing on our future, like interviews or exams, are also very stressful, as are

ones that give rise to frustration: a form of anger that is caused when something interferes with progress or reaching a desired goal. The blockage can be an emotional one, ensuing perhaps from work colleagues not accepting new proposals, or a partner who simply isn't listening. Or it can be physical, like a traffic jam or an appliance that won't work properly

Situational stressors that are themselves physical include bacteria, heat or cold, injury, pain or strain. For example, taking part in competitive sports, vigorous exercise, or carrying out physically demanding tasks are all potentially stressful. But stress may be self-induced through overworking or neglecting our bodies, or actually harming them. Physical assault by another person, or the fear of it, naturally engenders a very powerful stress reaction, with the urge to either fight or run. And when there has been severe trauma, through attack, accident or injury, or through having witnessed a frightening or disturbing incident, it can give rise to the classic post-traumatic stress disorder.

### Encounter Stress

While situational stress often involves people, encounter stress is that which arises from being in constant contact with others. It is stressful because this threatens the soul's need for space. It produces an inner tension that makes us want to get away from everyone, and be alone. The urge to escape is felt even when the relationships are harmonious, because the accumulation of human contact sooner or later leads to our exceeding our comfort zone. Those, like restaurant staff, air cabin attendants, or bank tellers, whose work is people-related, are more prone to encounter stress than employees who need only intermittent contact with others.

Especially vulnerable are those whose work involves helping people who are demanding or distressed, unpredictable or aggressive. This is why people in caring professions are at risk of developing stress-related illnesses. But in any job, pressure or threat can come from employers or managers. Having to face a boss who is likely to be critical, disapproving, challenging or confrontational creates anxiety, which in turn triggers the fight or flight reaction.

Encounter stress occurs not only in work situations, but also in the home. This may be because of constant arguments or hostility, conflicting requirements, overcrowding, or living in a densely populated area. Those who live in tower blocks, with people above, below and all around, are particularly prone to encounter stress, especially if there are also problems with neighbours. Living in close proximity to people who are unfriendly or aggressive is a double stressor as this gives rise to a combination of situational and encounter stress. For example, a neighbour who repeatedly parks in front of your drive, preventing you from getting to work, or one who constantly plays loud, intrusive music, causes stress-provoking anger, frustration and feelings of helplessness. And when there is no control over the timing of others' aggravating behaviour, the stress level soars.

**Time Stress**

We are living in an age that is governed by time. In the Western world especially, we live by the clock, dashing from one appointment to another, trying to fit as much into the day as possible. Time stress is even woven into the language. We constantly talk about time: having time, saving time, killing time, gaining time, losing time, making up for lost time.... Being pressured by time creates feelings of anxiety, helplessness and even despair, again leading to the typical biochemical fight or flight reaction.

In the business world, the principle time stressor is the deadline. Getting something done within a certain time frame is often considered more important than improving the quality of work. And the most vulnerable are the middle managers because they have to ensure that their subordinates meet the deadlines whilst also having to meet their superiors' demands. Writers who have to produce a set amount of work every week or month are also very susceptible to time stress, although in their case it is just as likely to be self-induced. In the home as well as the workplace, many people nowadays feel guilty and anxious if they haven't achieved a certain amount of work in any one day, and they imagine dire consequences if they fail to reach their own unrealistic targets.

## Anticipatory Stress

A lot of stress is anticipatory, and it comes from one's own imagination. The pressurising or threatening situation is pictured in the mind, producing a feeling of overload, fear or worry in advance. Particularly feared are hospital appointments, exams, interviews and board meetings; and often a person will face the same eventuality over and over, perhaps visualising different scenarios of everything that could possibly go wrong. The more prone one is to anticipatory stress, the longer the period for worrying before the actual event takes place. Since the fight or flight reaction is set into motion by internal images just as it is by actual events, anticipatory stress is more likely to be chronic.

When there is a tendency to always expect the worst, or a vulnerability to situational, encounter or time stress, it is probably because of having experienced disturbing or traumatic events in the past, particularly in childhood. Therefore, as well as being aware of your specific current stressors, you also need to understand how you may have been conditioned to cope – or not cope – with the normal ups and downs of life. We will begin by looking at four root causes of stress: low self-esteem, repressed anger, false guilt and generalised fear. If, as a child, you experienced abuse of any kind, were rejected or constantly criticised, you will probably identify all four as relevant to your own struggles, because the four are mutually dependent.


## ROOT CAUSES

### Damaged Self-esteem

The foundations of self-esteem are laid down in childhood, and any damage occurring during the developmental years will, if untreated, make one more prone to stress or depression in later life. A healthy self-esteem means, basically, that a person has a true sense of his own worth, secure in the knowledge that he is loved and approved. He will be able to realistically assess his own strengths and weaknesses, utilise his strengths and work at overcoming his weaknesses. Mistreatment of any kind damages self-esteem because it gives a child the subliminal message that he is unloved, unaccepted and disapproved of. And when there is constant criticism or ridicule, he also feels that he will never measure up or get it right. It is particularly damaging if a child is told that he is bad, stupid or ugly, or that he will never amount to anything.

Sometimes, an adult may not realise that he was damaged in childhood because the verbal put-downs were more subtle. For instance, self-esteem can be eroded by parents making unrealistic demands, drawing attention to the negative, or making comments like, "You did well, but...". These are all guaranteed to deflate a child's sense of his own worth and make him more prone to stress in later life. Self-esteem is also damaged through parents provoking sibling rivalry, focusing on grades, or valuing money, achievement or success above the spiritual or aesthetic. In these instances, the parents are also likely to have been poor role models. Paradoxically, being put on a pedestal and idealised by parents can also damage self-esteem, because the child is then unable to realistically assess his own abilities, and he cannot live up to the impossible standards imposed on him.

Low self-esteem, from whatever cause, makes a person vulnerable to all kinds of stress. This is partly because of deep-rooted feelings of inferiority which come from being put down or unrealistically exalted, or from being an outcast or misfit. All of these may lead to a stronger drive to prove oneself and be accepted, and a greater propensity to be frustrated by setbacks and overwhelmed by failure. Encounter stress is particularly hard to cope with because of shyness, difficulty valuing one's own opinions and judgements, dissatisfaction with one's physical appearance, and the false belief that others are more knowledgeable, intelligent, or just out to get you. A negative self-image also makes a person more sensitive to others' hurtful comments and more likely to take things the wrong way. He will probably have difficulty handling constructive criticism or dealing with conflict, and will find making decisions more stressful than the average person.

The need to demonstrate what they know deep down is the truth, that they are not stupid or incapable, also makes people with low self-esteem particularly susceptible to time stress; while the old voices from the past that tell them they are no good, that nothing will ever go right for them or they won't measure up, makes anticipatory stress inevitable.

In summary, low self-esteem gives people a distorted view of themselves, others and God, and make them act in ways that reinforce their misconceptions. For instance, their hypersensitivity to others' perceived put-downs will ultimately drive people away, making them feel more lonely, more different, and more convinced that they will never be loved and approved of. And so, their self-esteem is reduced even further. They are caught in a downward spiral that is threatening and frightening, as well as frustrating, and therefore highly stressful.

**Repressed or Overt Anger**
Children who are consistently hurt by grown-ups naturally become angry and frustrated. But they may not be able to express their feelings for fear of repercussions. And when it isn't safe to express anger, it has to be suppressed: consciously pushed down. In time, the suppression of anger can become so habitual that

a person no longer knows that he is doing it. The anger is then termed "repressed". Anger that is unknowingly kept inside naturally builds up, making a person respond more quickly to people or situations that create a fight reaction.

Repressed anger can build up for reasons other than abuse or overt criticism. For example, parents can create anger in their children by manipulating them, with comments like, "If you are not good I will be ill, and you won't have a mother any more." Or, they may give their children the impression that all anger is wrong. This is more likely to happen in Christian households, and then the children suppress – and later repress – anger because they feel guilty about their normal aggressive or vindictive feelings. In adult life it is then particularly hard for them to deal with current situations that create anger, or even to admit to themselves that they are angry.

To make matters worse, people who have been repressing anger for a long time have a high anger base level, so they boil over much more quickly than the average person when faced with irritating or annoying situations. This is because anger that is denied or unconsciously turned in on oneself is uncontrolled, therefore destructive. Anger is a very powerful form of energy; and, like any other form, such as wave power, the wind or electricity, can be used for good, to bring about positive changes. But when anger is unrecognised and unharnessed it churns around inside, causing tension; and the feeling of being out of control and constantly on the verge of disaster adds to the stress. When, inevitably, the anger seeps out or erupts, it destroys relationships, creating guilt and damaging personal integrity.

**False and True Guilt**

People who have been ill-treated in childhood have a tendency to feel guilty, even when they haven't done anything wrong. This, as opposed to the guilt that occurs because of one's own destructive behaviour – which also leads to stress – is false guilt. Children who are mishandled are unable to reason that their parents may be stressed, inadequate or insensitive, or have unresolved problems from their own childhoods. So, the children blame themselves. By the time they are able to recognise, usually in their early teens, that it is their parents who are at fault, the sense of guilt has taken such a hold that it cannot easily be shifted. Unlike true guilt which, if acted on, leads to a resolution of the problem – through, for instance, confession to God, apologising or making reparation – false guilt does not achieve anything. Instead, it remains inside, a constant heavy feeling that makes life more difficult than it need be, and creating feelings of depression or stress.

When there has been abuse of any kind, the sense of false guilt is particularly strong. Abused children feel guilty for many reasons: because of the abuse itself, because they failed to stop it, or because they reported it and broke up the family. With sexual abuse especially, there may be self-condemnation for having supposedly been in the wrong place at the wrong time, worn the wrong clothes or acted seductively. There may also be false guilt for having experienced sexual arousal during abusive incidents. In all these cases, the guilt is likely to be manifested in a tendency to run from life, and hide away.

Children who have been constantly criticised, being made to feel that they will never reach their parents' or teachers' standards — whether academically, physically or morally — are likewise prone to false guilt. In this instance, it is usually demonstrated by a constant drive to prove themselves, to do better and achieve more in order to gain recognition, acceptance and approval. When the drive to succeed is fuelled by false guilt it is unhealthy, and in many cases is an underlying component of the Type A personality. It creates stress because of the tremendous pressure placed on oneself, the forced demands of maintaining one's achievements, and the high cost of failure. False guilt and a fear of failure generally go together.

**Generalised Fear**

When children experience or witness violence, are exposed to frequent arguments, are expected to fulfil impossible demands, or are constantly threatened with punishment – by parents, bogey-men or God – they grow up feeling afraid. Fear is also triggered when the hurts are unintentional, and when they are more subtle and hidden, such as being compared unfavourably with a sibling, being treated as the baby of the family, or generally not being considered to have thoughts or opinions worth listening to. Or the fear may have arisen because of events occurring outside the home through, for instance, having been teased or bullied at school, or because of racial or sexual discrimination.

By adulthood, a specific fear of an aggressive mother, autocratic father, intimidating teacher or whatever may have become generalised. The victims then fear all authority figures, or all forms of criticism or confrontation. Or they may be afraid of meeting new people, going to new places, facing new challenges; or feel anxious about getting it wrong and being punished, disapproved of or disliked. When fear becomes all-pervasive it no longer serves its useful function: making one fight or flee from a threatening person or situation. Instead, there is a constant sense of danger, even when no danger exists, and a persistent feeling of stress.

If, during the developmental years especially, you experienced trauma of any kind, or any ongoing mistreatment, you will possibly have developed a vulnerability to all kinds of stress. And since the deep-rooted causes – low self-esteem, repressed anger, false guilt and generalised fear – to a large extent overlap, you will need to tackle all the roots, as well as learning how to cope with current stressors as and when they arise. At the same time, it will help if you can recognise your own hidden motives for pursuing a life-style that actually induces stress.


## UNRECOGNISED MOTIVES

### The Question of Motives

We all have mixed motives for everything we do. And we are often not aware of our own ulterior aims or hidden agendas. Like everyone else, there will be some needs and motives, both positive and negative, that you will be fully aware of. Others may be subconscious — just below the surface, therefore partially accessible. And yet others will be unconscious. With the last there will be total ignorance of any ulterior motives, in which case the following section will not trigger any immediate response.

However, if you are open to discovering new facets of truth about yourself, this section can begin the process of bringing unconscious needs and motives to the surface. The more recognition there is of underlying processes, the more you will be able to address them, and so prevent or reduce the tendency to expose yourself to the very stressors that your conscious self is trying to avoid. Unconscious motives can be divided into four main groups.

**The Need for High Drama**

The need to create high drama out of mundane situations is most likely to exist when there has been a history of not being noticed or listened to. This need will be manifested in a tendency to go over the top when annoyed or frustrated: shouting, screaming or crying. Small accidents or disappointments will be turned into major catastrophes, mild rebukes or criticism into unbearable hurt, and physical discomfort into debilitating illness, with possible psychosomatic symptoms. There will also be a propensity to create drama through causing arguments, provoking others to anger, or driving people away so that, like a tragedy queen, a person can bewail the inevitable loss. If this need is entirely unconscious, there will be no awareness that he is actually creating stress – and that part of him wants to create it.

The volatile and destructive behaviour that results from the partially recognised or unconscious desire to create high drama will continue the patterns of not being noticed or listened to. Others will tend to ignore you until you fly off the handle, have a crying fit, threaten suicide, or actually do become ill. And then, having got some response through your acting out, you will be further motivated to continue this extremely stressful behaviour.

**The Need to be Special**

The need to be set apart from the rest of humanity also arises from being ignored or neglected in childhood, or through not being allowed to be oneself, perhaps because of being a replacement for a dead sibling or having to fulfil a parent's frustrated ambitions. There is usually some awareness of this need, but there may be a failure to recognise its extent or how it is manifested. The drive to be the most successful, the cleverest or most talented, or to have the biggest house or car, may be motivated in part because of the need to be special. The desire to always be centre stage, whether in a work, social or family setting, may also arise from this deep-rooted need. A more subtle manifestation is the wish to be recognised for having endured pain and hardship, or even to be set apart through suffering. But particularly damaging, and stressful, is the need to be kept on a pedestal and worshipped by another human being.

However the need to be special is shown, the constant striving to be the best, and the effort needed to hog the limelight or remain on a pedestal will keep you in a constant state of tension. And the frustrated reactions of others, their weariness or disillusionment, and the inevitable setbacks and disappointments will create yet more stress. You will be caught on a treadmill from which there seems to be no escape, relationships will be spoiled, and you will become, at times, disillusioned and disgusted with yourself, creating a need to punish yourself.

**The Need to be Punished**

The unconscious need to be punished can ensue from current feelings of dislike for oneself, because of one's own behaviour or appearance. But it is mostly connected with low self-esteem and a tendency to false guilt. It arises when a child feels that he is to blame for being physically or sexually abused, criticised or put down, or when he has been held responsible for things that are not his fault, such as his parents' unhappy marriage. The negative view of self and the underlying guilt, if unresolved, may contribute towards being accident-prone, or a tendency to be drawn to dangerous jobs or take unnecessary risks. It is also likely to lead to provocative behaviour: actions that cause others to act punitively and so relieve the guilt. They may do this through getting angry with you, perhaps to the extent of being physically violent, using you sexually, verbally attacking you, despising or rejecting you.

When others respond negatively to your aggravating or seductive behaviour, their actions, being threatening and frightening, will naturally set off the fight or flight reaction. And their anger, abuse, contempt or whatever will reinforce your negative view of yourself and make you feel more, rather than less, guilty. So you will have a greater need to be punished. This downward spiral will create more and more stress, making it increasingly harder to avoid or cope with. In addition, there will be a constant feeling of inner tension because of the need to punish yourself being in conflict with the innate need to protect yourself.

## The Need to be a Rescuer

When someone has been damaged in childhood, there is often an unconscious need to vicariously care for oneself through meeting the needs of others. So there is a tendency to gravitate towards disadvantaged people, especially those who have been brought up in similar circumstances, and to attempt to rescue them from the effects of their dysfunctional family backgrounds. People in caring professions may be partly motivated by this unconscious need in themselves. But perhaps the most vulnerable are those who have difficulty saying no, and who therefore become worn out looking after needy friends and neighbours. The constant demands of others and the lack of time for themselves, the inevitable feelings of resentment this causes, and the mental and physical exhaustion all lead to chronic stress. There is a constant urge to battle through, and a constant desire to run away from it all. One part of the self recognises its own need for time and space, while another part, fuelled by false guilt, demands increasingly more time and effort for others, until there is nothing left to give.

Since we all have buried needs and motives, we are all driven, to some extent, by the unconscious desire to compensate for some deficiency in our own lives. But, we are also guided by our knowledge of ourselves and our interests and abilities. So, if you enjoy the buzz of a dangerous job or the satisfaction of being in a caring profession, it doesn't necessarily mean that your prime motivation consists of unmet childhood needs. However, it is important that you do recognise any underlying motives and that you get your deepest needs met in healthy ways that do not expose yourself, or others, to unnecessary stress.

Perhaps the best way to begin resolving your own needs is to look at how others have coped with pressure and threat. We might be living in a particularly stressful era, but people have experienced stress from the beginning of time, and it helps to know that others have been there, and to discover how they worked through the pain of abuse or rejection and learned to trust themselves, other people and God. The Bible is full of such examples: ordinary men and women whose struggles with fearsome enemies and adverse circumstances were compounded by their own doubts and fears, but who were able to find peace of mind in the midst of turmoil. They have given us perfect examples, not only of how to manage stress, but also of how to grow beyond it into a place of peace and serenity.

# 3

## EXAMPLES AND INSPIRATION

### HOW OTHERS CAN HELP

#### Providing Relief

When someone is going through a stressful situation, it is natural to want to talk about it, not primarily to find answers, but in order to offload. Talking is a natural stress-reliever, and when times are hard there is often a need to talk about the same thing over and over until it has been worked through the system. It is particularly helpful if the person chosen to unburden oneself to is able to listen, be understanding and empathic, and doesn't give advice – unless it is asked for.

When two people are experiencing the same stressors at the same time, it helps to be able to share one's feelings of anger, frustration, anxiety or whatever. Christians are often reticent to do this, and it has been known for people to rebuff those needing to offload with the dictum, "Is it true? Is it kind? Is it necessary?" It actually is necessary to talk, whether about a boss who is too demanding or overly critical, a mutual friend who has acted in a hurtful way, or even someone in authority in Christian circles who is causing confusion and upset. It is not unkind if the shared experiences remain confidential, and if the purpose is to relieve each other's stress, freeing the mind to look at possible solutions.

#### Supplying Answers

People who are stressed do not need impatient reproofs or simplistic answers, such as, "You need to do some assertiveness training," or "Just trust the Lord and everything will be alright." Such admonitions are in themselves stressful; they add to the pressure, creating feelings of failure and guilt. What stressed people do need is feedback about the others' experiences: to know how they perceive the situation and how they cope.

Often the answers come, not from family and friends, but from people in books. This is part of the reason why real-life stories truthfully told are so popular. The Bible is a collection of such stories. All of them honestly recount the doubts and fears, triumphs and failures, right- and wrongdoings of ordinary people. A classic example is the Psalmist David. He was often stressed – as well as depressed – because of his children causing trouble, friends letting him down, enemies hounding him, social injustice and political corruption. Sometimes he handled stress well; at other times he didn't. But he learned, in time, to grow beyond stress, so that he could take in his stride anything that came against him.

Throughout the history of Israel, stress often occurred on a national scale, as it did during the long period of captivity in Egypt. The Israelites were very understandably stressed because of their lack of freedom, their backbreaking work, their harsh treatment and their deferred hopes of freedom. Their unrelieved situation led them to feel that they were incapable of helping themselves. All they could do was look to God and pray for a deliverer.

On the domestic front, there is the story of the sisters, Mary and Martha. Jesus made a point of visiting them whenever he passed through their village and, on one of these occasions, Martha was bustling around in the kitchen making elaborate preparations for a meal, while Mary sat at Jesus' feet, listening to what he had to say. Martha was getting all hot and bothered, and eventually her resentment got the better of her. She complained to Jesus that she'd been left to do all the work, and she asked him to tell her sister to come and help. Jesus, who was undoubtedly enjoying Mary's company as she was his, kindly pointed out that Martha was worried and upset about many things, but that really there was only one thing needed. This, Mary had chosen, and he wasn't going to take it away from her. [1]

Sometimes, as with the children of Israel, stress arises because of the times in which we live – as discussed in Chapter 1. At other times, like Martha, we bring stress on ourselves because of failure to recognise what is really important. More usually, as with the Psalmist David, stress arises because of a combination of factors. If any of those cited were alive today they would understand many of today's stressors, and they would be able to help those experiencing pressure or threat, providing the relief of a listening ear, and some answers. In order to grasp more fully what those answers are, we will now look at three Bible characters who found themselves in very stressful situations: Moses, the slave girl Hagar, and Nehemiah.


## A LEADER'S BURDEN

### Moses' Troubles

God had told Moses to lead his people, the children of Israel, out of Egypt, where they had been slaves for the past four hundred years. But Moses didn't want this responsibility, and he took it on very reluctantly. And right from the start there was trouble. When, full of fear and foreboding, he went to ask Pharaoh's permission to lead the Israelites into the desert to make sacrifices, Pharaoh refused and made life harder than ever for his slaves – who turned against Moses, blaming him for their added misfortunes. And when, after a series of plagues, Pharaoh finally relented, Moses found himself and his charges trapped between the Red Sea and the pursuing Egyptians, with nowhere to turn. However, God miraculously brought them safely across and they were able to begin their long journey towards the Promised Land. And that was when Moses really began to experience the burden of leadership.

First, they wandered for three days in the wilderness of Shur without finding water. And when at last they discovered an oasis the people complained that the water was bitter. Later they grumbled that there was nothing much to eat, and they reminisced about the good old days back in Egypt when they'd had melons and cucumbers, leeks, onions and garlic. The next time they ran out of water they became so angry they wanted to stone Moses, who had to use all his resources to subdue them whilst also mustering an army to repel an attack by neighbouring Amalekites. Meanwhile, he was acting as a judge and arbitrator. From morning till night he was faced with a steady stream of people coming to him for help and advice, and wanting him to settle disputes.

God repeatedly provided the Israelites with food and water, and Moses hoped that these constant signs of his goodness would enable the people to start trusting in Jahweh. But when he went up Mount Sinai to receive the levitical laws, including the Ten Commandments, the people made an image of God in the form of a golden calf, an Egyptian symbol of strength. Moses was so incensed by their limited concept of God that he smashed the tablets of stone on which the commandments were written – a sure sign of stress.

Having led the people for many more years, and supervised the making and setting up of the tabernacle in the wilderness, Moses was now opposed by his own brother and sister, who objected to his foreign wife. He had no sooner sorted this problem when ten spies he had sent out brought back frightening reports of the inhabitants of Canaan, and the people once again rebelled, this time to the extent of wanting to choose a new leader to take them back to Egypt. There were more problems when people he had appointed as community leaders rose up against him, accusing him of arrogance. And when the people complained yet again about lack of water, Moses finally had enough of them. Although God had told him to speak to a rock, from which water would subsequently flow, Moses instead hit the rock while speaking angrily to the rebels.

Nearing the promised land of Canaan at last, the leader of the country of Edom denied them passage, so they had to go the long way round. There was more hassle, more enemies to contend with, but at last they were ready to cross over the River Jordan into Canaan. Because of his angry outburst, Moses wasn't allowed to enter. He died on Mount Nebo, at the age of 120, looking out on the land of promise.

## Moses' Stressors

During the forty years it took them to reach Canaan there were periods of relative stability and calm. There were oases in the desert, rich with produce after the winter rains, but there were many bad times when food and water were scarce, when the people complained and mutinied, and when there were threats and attacks from other nomadic tribes. During these bad times Moses experienced a combination of situational and encounter stress. Even when he wasn't having to deal with grumbling and rebellion, he was in constant demand as an arbitrator and law-giver. If he experienced time stress it was in the form of anxiety about finding provisions, wondering what would happen if they didn't reach the next oasis before food ran out, or if there would be sufficient rain. As a leader, Moses had an entire nation to worry about.

At the beginning especially, Moses also experienced anticipatory stress. When God called him from the burning bush and told him to go and face Pharaoh, Moses had been living in Midian for forty years, and he had a growing family to think of. He didn't want to uproot, certainly not to return to Egypt where, having killed an Egyptian overseer, he had been forced to leave under very perilous circumstances. He also lacked confidence in his speaking ability and, at first, he needed his brother Aaron to do all the talking. He couldn't imagine speaking to Pharaoh himself and achieving any kind of success.

## Moses' Answers

Following his confrontations with Pharaoh, Moses' first big test was the Red Sea. There was no way they could get across. Flight was impossible, and Pharaoh and his army were in hot pursuit. But Moses was able to say to the people, "The Lord will fight for you, and you have only to be still." [2]

He had, by now, enough experience of danger to be able to stay calm in a crisis and let God work things out. Moses had also become convinced of his own calling; he knew that he was the right man for the job, and this too enabled him to keep his stress level to a minimum. When, for instance, 250 Israelites, led by Korah, accused Moses of lording it over them and told him to resign, he naturally felt threatened and was angry with them. But rather than fighting them, he asked God to vindicate him and establish his position as leader.

Moses was described as a humble man – more humble than anyone else on the face of the earth. And this, perhaps more than anything, enabled him to cope with stress. When his brother and sister complained about his marrying a foreigner, and reminded him that he wasn't God's only mouthpiece, Moses was ready to listen to them. Again, he didn't feel the need to fight in order to retain his position. Neither did he feel that he had to be the only one with spiritual gifts. Rather, he wished that everyone had similar endowments. His humility also enabled him to delegate as his father-in-law, Jethro, suggested when he paid them a visit. They were then encamped at an oasis, and Moses was tied up all day with the lines of people coming to him for help and advice. Jethro pointed out that what Moses was doing wasn't good: the work was too heavy, and there was no way he could handle it alone — not without wearing himself out. [3]

Moses, then, coped because of his increasing confidence in himself, his helpers and God, and because of his organising skills and humility. His lack of false pride, which often arises because of insecurity, enabled him to listen and delegate, and released him from the drive to prove himself and stay at the top. Since Moses' stressors are not very different from those we experience today, you can learn through his story how to begin developing faith in yourself, as well as other people and God. As faith increases, you will acquire a sense of inner calm that will make it easier to let go of the need to do it all, and reduce the urge to keep fighting in order to achieve recognition or success. Instead, you will be able to conserve your energy to deal more effectively with unavoidable stress.


## A SERVANT'S PLIGHT

### Hagar's Dilemma

Hagar's stress was very different, and much of hers was unnecessary. She was an Egyptian slave, a maidservant to Sarai, the wife of the patriarch Abraham. It has been speculated that she had obtained her name, which means "flight" or "runaway", because of having run away from a former Egyptian mistress, and that Sarai came across her during a visit to Egypt. She was now living far from her childhood home, but Abraham was a very rich and important man so Hagar would have lived comfortably. And since Sarai was a kind woman, she was probably treated well. Then something happened that changed Hagar's world.

Sarai was unable to conceive and, according to the custom of the day, she asked her husband to produce a child by her maidservant. The child would belong to Sarai and be Abraham's legal heir. Although this was an accepted undertaking, it placed both women in a difficult position, which Hagar did not handle well. When she knew that she was pregnant she despised her mistress, treating her contemptuously. Sarai was naturally upset and complained about it to her husband, who told her to do whatever she liked with Hagar. So, Sarai began mistreating her. Eventually the abuse became too much for Hagar and, living up to her name, she fled.

Presumably Hagar was trying to get back to her original home in Egypt, because an angel of the Lord found her near a spring in the desert, by the road to Shur. This is west of Canaan where Abraham was then living. The angel told Hagar that God knew of her misery, but that she was to return to Sarai and submit to her. The angel also told her that God would make of her expected child a great nation. As a result of this encounter,

Hagar gave God the name, "El Roi", which is generally taken to mean "a God of seeing", but is more accurately translated, "a God who permits himself to be seen". Hagar was astounded that Abraham's God should take notice of her, and that she should have experienced a visitation from God and lived.

Hagar obeyed the angel and went back to her mistress. Her son, Ishmael, which means "God hears", was born, and she now found herself in an even more difficult position. Until then she had been a servant, but now, as mother of the heir, she had a very exalted role. And, as events proved, she never quite managed to adjust: her pride always got the better of her. Ishmael was about thirteen when Sarai, now renamed Sarah, gave birth to her own son, Isaac. And the problems between the two women started all over again. On the day Isaac was weaned, at age two or three, Abraham gave a great feast, and during the festivities Sarah noticed that Ishmael was mocking her son. She was furious and told Abraham to get rid of Hagar and the boy, saying that she would never share her son's inheritance with the son of a slave woman. So, having been reassured by God, Abraham reluctantly did what his wife wanted. And once again, Hagar found herself out in the wilderness.

Before Hagar and Ishmael left, Abraham had provided them with food and water. But the supplies soon ran out. And when, in a state of exhaustion, Ishmael collapsed, Hagar left him under a bush and sat some distance away, so that she wouldn't see him die. Then she broke down and sobbed. But then, just as on the previous occasion, an angel came to her rescue, pointing out a nearby well. Hagar refilled the water skins and, having been refreshed, she and her son went on their way. They settled in the desert where Ishmael became a great archer. He later married an Egyptian and, as the angel had promised, became the father of a great race: the present-day Arabs.

**Hagar's Stressors**

Hagar's stress began with a complex situation. Bearing the master's son placed her in a kind of in-between world where she was neither one thing nor the other. She no longer belonged with the servants, but neither did she belong with her master and mistress. Hagar must have felt very confused and lonely. But, she brought much of her stress upon herself because of the contemptuous way she treated her mistress. This led to severe encounter stress; and the combination of too little contact with people she could relate to, and the daily exposure to Sarai's coldness and abuse, drove her into flight.

When, years later, Hagar was banished into the wilderness, she experienced situational stress in the form of physical hardship. She was exposed to the hot desert sun, suffering from extreme thirst, and she was physically and mentally exhausted. The water situation also created time stress: she had only a limited time in which to find a spring or well. If she failed, she and her son would face certain death. The anticipation of death, both for herself and her son, was undoubtedly the worst stress of all.

**Hagar's Help**

As an Egyptian, Hagar would have worshipped the gods and goddesses of Egypt. She may have embraced her mistress's faith, but if so she probably thought of their God as being a regional one – just as the gods of Egypt were. Hence her amazement when, prior to Ishmael's birth, God saw her in the wilderness somewhere between Abraham's country and her own. This and the angel's assurance that she would be the mother of a great nation gave her the courage she needed to go back. The visitation must also have reminded her that she had someone else to think about, other than herself. The angel also told Hagar how to behave on her return: she was to submit to Sarai, treating her mistress with the respect she deserved.

Because of the help she received, Hagar stopped running, turned around, and went back to the situation she had once considered unbearable. And so she changed the course of history. Hagar also tried to obey the angel's command to defer to her mistress. But here she didn't entirely succeed. Her son's open mockery of Isaac years later must have been learned from his mother, and it was this that led to her final banishment. But when, on the point of death, Hagar was once again helped by an angel, who pointed out the well of water, she went on to take the practical steps of finding somewhere to live and some means of support. Later, she set about finding a wife for her son who, already, had become a great man.

Hagar was not at first a believer; she had no one to turn to in her distress. But the fact that she didn't believe made no difference: God saw her anyway. During times of stress it is reassuring to know that God sees and that, however weak our faith, he wants to come to our aid. Your angel may not be a literal one; it may appear in the form of a good friend, an unexpected letter, a sudden change of circumstances. But, however the assistance comes, it will come. Bad times don't last forever, and it will help if you can remind yourself of this; also of the fact that, during times of stress, it is often impossible to see the solution, even when it is right there in front of you. This will give you the impetus needed to open your eyes to new possibilities and take charge of your own destiny, rather than passively accepting whatever life throws at you. But you should do this in a spirit of humility. With the right attitude and response you can avoid a lot of unnecessary stress.

## A REFORMER'S RESPONSIBILITY

### Nehemiah's Task

Nehemiah, was someone who knew exactly how to reduce his stress level. He was a captive exiled Jew, cupbearer to the Persian King, Artaxerxes I (465-425 BC). This was a privileged position, but also a stressful one: it was part of his job to taste the king's wine for poison. During his exile, Nehemiah heard news of the desolation of his home capital, Jerusalem: the razed walls still hadn't been repaired and the city was vulnerable to attack. Nehemiah was so upset he was unable to hide his feelings from the king, and as having a miserable expression was an offence punishable by death, naturally he was afraid. However, the king was surprisingly understanding and gave Nehemiah permission to return to his own country, granted him safe passage, and made him governor, so that he could supervise the rebuilding of the walls.

Back in Jerusalem, being then doubtful of his reception, Nehemiah inspected the walls at night, under cover of darkness. Then he encouraged those who had survived the exile to set about rebuilding, and got them organised. They had a limited amount of time in which to repair the walls and replace the gates, which had been burned, and it seemed an impossible task. Added to this, they were constantly being harassed by three officials. One of them, Sanballat the Horonite, mocked the "feeble Jews" for thinking they could bring stones back to life from heaps of burned rubble. [4] And Tobiah the Ammonite added scathingly that, if even a fox climbed up on their newly built wall, it would fall down. [5]

As well as having to cope with constant mockery and discouragement, the builders were also under physical attack. So Nehemiah had to organise a guard. Meanwhile, he was repeatedly distracted by messages from Sanballat, Tobiah and Geshem the Arab, enticing him to a meeting in a village on the plain outside. Suspecting that they meant to harm him, Nehemiah ignored the first four letters but read the fifth, which stated falsely that he was plotting a revolt with the aim of setting himself up as king of Judah: an act of treason. There was also a frightening report that men were coming to kill him. As if this wasn't enough, Nehemiah, like Moses, was constantly under pressure from the locals to sort out their financial difficulties, settle arguments, correct injustices and make reforms.

### Nehemiah's Stressors

Nehemiah was subjected to all four kinds of stressor. His situation as exiled cupbearer to the Persian king was stressful, and his position as governor of Jerusalem even more so. There he experienced adverse physical conditions, having to work secretly during the cold of night, then throughout the relentless heat of day. And he had a daunting task, a very high workload and unskilled helpers who needed constant supervision. His workers were willing and eager, but they were not trained as builders; they included priests and rulers, with their sons and daughters.

Nehemiah also experienced contact overload. Not only did he have to organise the builders, but he also had to deal with a stream of people coming to him with a backlog of complaints, queries and complex social problems. And he felt constantly frustrated and angry at the mistreatment of the poor. In addition, he had to contend with the continual presence of Sanballat and his associates and listen to their endless taunts and threats. And he never knew where, when and how they would attack him next.

Nehemiah was also exposed to time pressure: while the walls were broken down and the gates missing the city remained vulnerable to attack. So there was not a moment to waste. The task was accomplished in an amazing 52 days, during which time Nehemiah must also have experienced anticipatory stress, wondering if he and the Jews would be able to keep their work from being sabotaged, if the rumours about him wanting to be king would be believed and acted on, and if there actually were men coming to kill him. Perhaps he also wondered if he would die before he could carry out his commission.

### Nehemiah's Coping Strategies

Nehemiah's method of coping with the very stressful situation he found himself in could be summed up as: trust, obey, and keep your sword ready. Nehemiah was a man of prayer, and he believed implicitly that God would protect him and his people, and provide the wisdom and strength necessary to complete the task. Nehemiah also believed in himself. He knew that he was in the right place at the right time, and that what he was doing was good and just. He could, therefore, rest in God, knowing that whatever happened, the Lord was in control.

As well as being a man of prayer, with implicit trust in God and belief in his own abilities, Nehemiah was also a good organiser, so he was able to deal with each stressor as and when it arose. He also knew which stressors to fight, and which to flee from. He chose to ignore the taunts of Sanballat and his associates, and encouraged his workers to do likewise. He also chose to ignore Tobiah's letters. But when the attacks on the builders and himself became physical, Nehemiah set about posting a guard, on duty day and night. This meant reorganising his builders into two groups. Half, making up the guard, were equipped with spears, shields, bows and arrows. The other half carried on with the building. But even they had their swords at hand, ready to fight if necessary.

When the walls were completed, Nehemiah called on Ezra the scribe to read to the assembled people the book of the law, and he led the people to pledge themselves to obey its commands. It was Nehemiah's belief that God had established laws to keep his people safe, just as good parents make rules to keep their children from getting hurt. So, he could return to Persia in the sure knowledge that, as long as the Jews continued to obey God's commands, the reforms he had begun would be maintained. This inner assurance enabled Nehemiah to relinquish the burden of responsibility and, although he had to carry out fresh reforms when he made another visit to Jerusalem some years later, he was not weighed down by the failures of others. He had done his part, and that was enough.

During times of stress, it is well to ask yourself if, like Nehemiah, you believe in what you are doing, if your work is fulfilling, and if you have a good relationship with family and colleagues. Question also your belief in God. Do you really believe that he is right there with you in your situation? If so, this knowledge will enable you to retain a sense of inner calm, no matter how difficult things are. It also helps if, like Nehemiah, you can clearly see incipient stress in your life and decide which people and situations to confront and which to avoid.

Perhaps you have been able to relate especially to Nehemiah, and been inspired by his faith and approved his perceptiveness and down to earth practicality. Or maybe you have identified more with Moses or Hagar, or with some other historical figure whose ability to deal with extremely stressful situations has aroused your admiration and respect. Your identification with someone who has grown beyond stress into serenity, and an ability to learn from their mistakes as well as their coping strategies, is an important step towards reaching that place yourself. It also makes it easier for you to learn and implement the various stress management techniques that are still being taught today.

# 4

## STRESS MANAGEMENT

### DEVELOP AWARENESS

**Know Yourself**

In order to manage stress, the first requirement is to notice it. We often think that we are feeling calm and in control when actually we are in a state of high arousal. Monitoring yourself means not only noticing when you are stressed, but also recognising your own specific signs and symptoms, beginning with your feeling-set. For example, do your feelings generally revolve around anger: irritation, annoyance or frustration? Or are they associated with fear: worry, anxiety, panic? Also notice your general feeling-tendency. Do you, for instance, usually feel hemmed in and trapped, pushed down, overwhelmed, or as if you are drowning, floating on nothing, spinning out of control, caught up in a whirlwind...?

Note also your primary response: what you immediately feel like doing in moments of high stress. Do you want to sink through the floor, disappear, strike out, swear, scream, cry...? Practice detecting your feelings prior to facing a difficult situation, during the situation, and afterwards. This will show you, not only whether your stress is largely anticipatory, but also how quickly your body reverts to normal after the fight or flight reaction has occurred.

It is also important that you monitor your physical signs and symptoms. For you, stress might manifest itself mostly in headaches, or knotted stomach, bloated feeling or heartburn, a tendency to break out in a sweat, or a frequent need to urinate. Begin noting your reactions when you are confronted with a situation that you normally find stressful, such as going to work, facing a particular client, having to do a hated household chore, preparing for an exam.... As you become increasingly aware of

47

the effects of stress on your body, you will begin to detect the smaller changes; not just those that affect the major muscle groups.

You can assist your identification of, and response to, the minor changes in your body with the following exercise: before, during and after a stressful situation, sit quietly with your eyes closed and, working down the body, notice the sensations in your scalp, forehead, facial muscles, neck, shoulders, hands, and so on. Later, you will find yourself detecting these finer responses in situations that you didn't previously recognise as stressful.

In addition to observing your emotional and physical responses to stress, you should also monitor your general behaviour patterns. For instance, when you are stressed are you liable to increase alcohol consumption, smoke, stuff yourself with chocolate, or turn to chemicals such as sleeping tablets, aspirin or antacids? Do you tend to avoid company, or go where people are and act out of character: playing the fool, showing off, starting arguments, or being sexually provocative? Are you inclined to burst into tears, thump furniture, get loud, go quiet...? When you are able to quickly recognise your typical behaviours, feelings and physical changes in response to stress, you will be in a better position to identify, and deal with, those situations that create stress.

**Recognise the Stressors**

There are some situations that are obviously stressful, but others may not be so easy to detect. Begin by identifying the main category of stressor — situational, encounter, time stress and anticipatory stress — then break them down into smaller components. And remember, what is stressful for one person may be very stimulating and enjoyable to another. You need to know what is stressful for you.

At work, for instance, do you become stressed because of a high workload, because you don't have enough to do, or because the work is monotonous and undemanding? Is your particular stressor uncertainty: not knowing your job objectives and what is expected of you, getting unclear instructions, or living under the threat of transfer, relocation or redundancy? Do you perhaps cope badly with constant interruptions, frequent changes, too much responsibility, hassle from superiors or incompetence from subordinates? Maybe for you it is not getting feedback about your work that is the most stressful, or being unsure of your place in the work structure. Perhaps you handle criticism badly, don't cope well with confrontation, or find it difficult to say no? Or is it the physical conditions you find the most stressful: the central heating turned too high, a smoky atmosphere, excessive noise, poor lighting...?

A similar set of stressors concerning physical conditions, workload or monotony may exist in the home, especially for mothers of young children. But at home there may be additional stressors in the form of isolation from adult company and an unvarying domestic scene. Or perhaps most of your stress comes from having to juggle with children and outside work, or the guilt that arises from needing outside work to stay solvent or sane. Is it the children themselves who are causing the most stress? If so, what is it that especially gets to you? Is it their interrupting when you want to get things done, their whining, arguing, falling out with each other, refusing to obey...? Whatever your situation, recognising your own particular stressors is essential because only then will you be able to find ways of dealing with them; or better still, take steps to avoid them.


## ADAPT OR ALTER

### Change Yourself

In order to cope with stressful situations, you can basically do one of two things: either change yourself to fit the situation, or change the situation to fit yourself. Changing yourself may involve learning not to react to minor provocations but, rather, letting them pass. If you are able to do this, having first identified those things that are minor, you will be better able to take the more important things in your stride. Or, you can resolve to stop taking on unnecessary work, or decide that you don't always have to do things a certain way just because you, or your parents, have always done it that way.

Changing yourself can also mean learning to look at things differently. For instance, if you find a particular job boring, you can consider ways of approaching the work more creatively. Or, you can practice tackling mind-numbing chores in a less stressful way by simultaneously working at expanding your mind, perhaps through learning college material, memorising poetry, passages of the Bible or Shakespeare, or planning a meal or lecture. Or you can use the time to simply daydream. This can be very restful or conversely, very productive, leading you to connect memories that you previously thought had nothing in common, and to come up with new thoughts, ideas and plans.

If your stress comes primarily from people, then you can adapt by looking at others through different eyes. For example, you can practice focusing on their good points and finding things you like about them, rather than spotlighting the traits and behaviours you find irritating or intimidating. Also question your assumptions regarding others' motives. Do you, for instance, assume that people are deliberately ignoring you, or are out to get you? If so, then you are setting yourself up to be stressed and should start considering other, more likely, reasons for their behaviour. You can also resolve to begin taking an interest in your acquaintances, and getting to know them. This is especially helpful when you are afraid of people or feel insecure around them. Fear often arises because of not knowing, and it is a major cause of discrimination. If you can learn to see differences as interesting, and even exciting, then you will be freed from the stress of needing everyone to be the same.

You can also change yourself by learning how to communicate more effectively: to put across your thoughts, ideas and opinions and express your feelings in ways that produce a positive response – even if the other doesn't agree with you. This involves learning how to be clear and concise, confident and assured, open and friendly. And it necessitates being assertive and saying no, setting boundaries so that others don't intrude on your emotional and physical space. Above all, you will need to change any tendency to bottle up stressful feelings and start opening up to people, allowing them to help and support you. Opening up means also being able to listen: to hear what another person is really saying, and to accept opposing views in a way that is non-judgemental, caring and understanding. You also need to develop empathy: the ability to see things from the others' point of view and imagine how a situation might feel for them.

Relationships often fail because of attempts to mould a spouse or partner to fit one's own personality and interests. But true love is freeing. It allows the other to develop in his own time and his own way. So, while working at changing yourself, always bear in mind that you can only change yourself – not anyone else. This means, in summary, reforming how you perceive people and situations, and how you relate to them. These changes are a necessary aspect of growth and development, and part of the process of growing beyond stress into serenity.

## Change the Situation

Although you cannot change other people, at least not in essentials, you can change the situation. In order to do this you first have to define your objectives: what you want to achieve. It may be to enhance working relationships, reduce your workload, improve the quality of your output, increase production.... Or it could be to balance your role as a mother with your need for adult company and mental stimulation. Having identified your goals, the next step is to set priorities: decide what is the most stressful and needs immediate resolution, and what can wait. There may then need to be a certain amount of reorganising before you can implement some strategies for reducing stress.

When stress arises because of work overload or time pressure, whether in a business setting or at home, the most effective strategy is to delegate. Or, you can find ways of breaking the work down into more manageable sections, being realistic about what can be accomplished in a set time and learning to pace yourself. Even as a fairly junior employee there will be something you can do to make work less stressful. It might mean requesting a transfer to another department, asking for more challenging work, changing your hours, or making some minor alterations to the work structure.

If your main stressors are physical ones, such as rush hour traffic, office temperature, noise or any kind of work hazard, you may be able to change the situation through finding practical solutions. The same applies if your stress is related to anxiety about social or political conditions. Do some brainstorming. That is, think of as many ideas as possible, no matter how ridiculous or outlandish, and write down everything that comes to mind. Then go through your list and choose those solutions that appear the most practicable. The mere fact of recognising that there is something you can do, no matter how minimal, and gaining some control over a situation will reduce the immediate stress level, and help diminish anticipatory stress.

If you experience contact overload, you can perhaps arrange times and places so that you are not constantly interrupted by other people's demands, or else start giving yourself frequent short breaks. Or you may need to confront someone you are having difficulties with. This is stressful, but not as stressful as burying emotions and living with unresolved conflict, coldness or contention. However, there are times when it is impossible to come to an understanding – whether with a partner, relative or friend, neighbour, boss or colleagues at work – it takes two. But in this case, you should ask yourself why you are allowing yourself to be used, disrespected or ignored. Deciding to leave a relationship if this involves a spouse or partner is a drastic step to take, and it may conflict with your values and beliefs. Nevertheless, it is important that you face your difficulties, and that one way or another you do something about them.

Deciding to leave a job you dislike also necessitates a major upheaval. But again, you need to recognise the true state of affairs. So, ask yourself, "Am I in the right job? Do I feel fulfilled and happy in my work? Am I going anywhere?" If the answer to any of these is no, then ask yourself what you really want to do. Begin by ascertaining whether you prefer working with people, things, or information. Then ask yourself what kind of atmosphere you like – indoors or outdoors, quiet or noisy, calm or bustling? Decide if you like to work on your own initiative or if you prefer a more structured setting, with people you can turn to for help and advice. Do you thrive on variety and challenge, or do you cope better with routine work? Think also about the long-term prospects. Do you really want to spend the best years of your life doing the same as you are right now? If not, what is keeping you from following your dreams? Is it fear of change, of failing, of losing your financial security? Staying in an unsuitable job can be far more stressful than taking a calculated risk and setting out into the unknown.

## LEARN TO UNWIND

### Practice Relaxation
However you decide to deal with a stressful situation, you can reduce your stress level by learning to unwind. Whether you carry out specific relaxation techniques or simply allow your body to loosen up and your mind to switch off, it actuates the parasympathetic nervous system: part of the body's homeostatic device. Relaxing, which means becoming less rigid or tense, lowers blood pressure, pulse and respiration rate, it normalises the digestive processes, increases the number of circulating lymphocytes, and enables you to think more clearly. If you choose to implement a relaxation method, there are basically two kinds that you can practice without professional assistance. One is known as the quickie relaxation technique. This takes only a few minutes so can be carried out at your desk at work, between household chores, or wherever you happen to be.

First sit comfortably and, if appropriate, loosen your clothes. Close your eyes, and take three deep breaths through the nose, exhaling slowly through the mouth. Then, breathing normally, slowly stretch, at the same time tightening your muscles. Now let your body go completely limp. Stay limp for about ten seconds, then slowly take three more deep breaths. You can assist the process by using mental imagery, imagining that your body is made of lead and is extremely heavy, or that your legs are made of jelly. You can carry out this sequence as many times as you like.

The second technique is progressive relaxation. Again, find a comfortable position, and take three deep breaths. Then, close your eyes and focus on a specific set of muscles in your body, beginning with your toes. As you concentrate, curl your

toes under, and then let them relax. Now bend up your feet —
and let them go. Next stiffen your calf muscles — and relax
them — and so on up the body, ending with the various groups of
muscles in your face: the jaw, around the eyes, forehead and
scalp. When you begin by tightening the muscles it enables them
to relax more fully, just as a pendulum swings further to the right
if it is first pulled to the left. This technique can take from fifteen
to thirty minutes, so you will need to get into the habit of setting
aside time for this, and for resting generally.

**Rest the Body and Soul**

In order to function well, we need to have periods of
rest, which means abstaining from exertion or employment. This
is why God told us to rest one day out of seven. It is a principle
that was to be adhered to whether or not there was still another
field to plough, or more crops to harvest. The work had to be left.
In this day and age especially, we have difficulty stopping. We
set ourselves deadlines and make ourselves keep going until the
project is complete. And there is a tendency to feel guilty if we
leave things undone. Women who work at home are especially
prone to this form of false guilt, not allowing themselves to
pause until the house is spotless, the shopping done and the
meals prepared. But remember the story of Mary and Martha.
Jesus commended Mary for making the best of their short time
together, sitting at his feet and listening, even though there was a
meal to get ready. The meal, he implied, could wait.

Resting means, first of all, making sure that you have
enough sleep. People vary in the amount of sleep they require, so
you will need to assess how much is right for you, and ensure
that you get it. If you have sleeping difficulties a slight change of
routine could help, like taking time to unwind before bedtime,
having a warm bath, or reading a favourite book. Avoid vigorous
exercise last thing at night as this stimulates the body, making it
difficult to close down for the night.

Rest also means ensuring that you have time for the things
you enjoy, like walking, sitting on the beach, or simply lying in
the garden. If you have a very busy lifestyle, just allowing
yourself ten minutes now and then to do absolutely nothing can

prevent overload. When you stop to enjoy the wonder of creation, your soul also is rested: it is given time and space and filled with the beauty on which it thrives. Also restful for the soul is music. But be careful in your choice of music. When your primary need is for repose, then choose music that is calm and relaxing, and with lyrics that do not over-stimulate an already exhausted mind.

**Release the Mind**

Learning to rest the mind is especially helpful for those in academic work or whose jobs demand mental concentration, and for people prone to anticipatory stress. You can create your own stressful situations by constantly thinking about bad experiences you have passed through, or worrying about things that might happen. So the more you can learn to release your mind from working overtime, the less stressed you will be. One technique is called thought stopping. When the same thoughts are going round and round in your head, simply call out, in your mind, the word "Stop!" This will cause your thoughts to jerk to a standstill, just long enough for you to set them off on a different track. You will need to keep practicing this one because, at first, after the momentary pause, your thoughts are likely to carry on as before.

Another technique is called rehearsal. If you have to face a stressful situation, such as an interview, then rehearse the entire scene in your mind, picturing yourself sounding assured, confidently answering questions, having alternative plans of action.... But you will need, first, to allow your mind to wander, imagining various scenarios, faces of people, room details and the like. This will enable you to recognise any omissions, such as necessary information you don't have to hand, or questions you might be asked that you don't have the answers to. Rehearsing stressful scenes in a positive manner will not only reduce anticipatory stress, it will also make you better prepared for success.

Desensitisation is a technique that is particularly used to reduce the stress that is associated with fear, such as fear of spiders, flying, being shut in.... To practice this, begin by relaxing your body, then imagine yourself facing your fear in stages. For instance, if you are afraid of flying, imagine yourself at first simply going to the airport. Picture yourself going through the doors, feeling calm, looking around with interest. Then visualise yourself watching aircraft taking off and landing, and make up stories about the passengers, the places they have come from, where they are going, whom they will be meeting. Next picture yourself calmly boarding the plane, sitting down, fastening your seat belt. Then see the plane taking off and imagine yourself enjoying the sensation, looking forward to your holiday. You can use this kind of mental imagery for any kind of stressful situation, taking your thoughts as far or as little as you want. Generally speaking, you are in control of your own thoughts.

Mental diversion, which is associated with meditation, is a thought technique that is used to replace stressful thoughts with relaxing ones. To do this you imagine yourself in a scene that is particularly restful for you – lying on a palm beach in the sun, sitting in a garden full of sweet-smelling flowers, floating on the sea or in the clouds, sitting by a cosy fire with the curtains closed while the wind howls outside.... You can think also about colours you find relaxing, or mentally quote Bible verses, snatches of poetry, passages of Shakespeare.... The Bible tells us to think about things that are true, noble, right, pure, lovely, admirable, excellent and praiseworthy. [6] We are meant to habitually focus our minds on what is good, true and beautiful, which means that we first have to experience such things. This is more than positive thinking; this kind of thinking also enriches the soul, the part of self that tends to get overlooked in this materialistic world, keeping us from living balanced and wholesome lives.


## ACQUIRE BALANCE

### Balance of Work and Play

In order to live lives that are not plagued by stress-related psychological and physical illness, you need to have balance: first, a balance of work and play. Play, in this sense, does not necessarily mean sitting on the floor with a train set! It means permitting yourself to do things just for the fun of it, to be spontaneous and free, and to allow yourself times to daydream and play around with thoughts and ideas. People who are prone to stress, and Type A personalities in particular, seem to find it especially difficult to play. They have a propensity to be workaholics, driving themselves harder and harder to achieve more and more in increasingly less time. And they cannot stop. If this is you, then even your so-called relaxation will be stressful because it is likely to be highly competitive, and it will need to have a purpose. So, you will be easily irritated when things get in the way. Work is necessary for our own well-being – as well as for financial reasons. But you must also learn to be child-like: to play because playing is fun.

### Balance of Challenge and Ease

As already noted, just as muscles need the right amount of tension to keep us upright, so we need a certain amount of emotional stress. And this can take the form of challenge. We have to challenge ourselves, to push ourselves harder, go a bit further, try something new, take risks, otherwise we stagnate. But challenge has to be balanced with times of ease, when we allow ourselves to saunter along at a leisurely pace with no specific goal in mind. If you are prone to stress, then maybe you panic during those times in life when you appear to be in a kind of limbo. But you need these transition periods because then you can stand still, reflect on where you have come from, grieve for what has ended, and decide where to go next. If you are constantly rushing into something new the moment you have reached a goal in life, you are heading for stress.

## Balance of Discipline and Self-indulgence

In order to meet your own, or others', challenges, a certain amount of self-discipline is required, and you may need to be hard on yourself, depriving yourself of things you would really like. This is essential for your emotional, mental and spiritual development. But if life consists of nothing but harsh self-discipline and deprivation, you will end up getting stressed. Discipline needs to be balanced with periods of self-indulgence. This does not mean doing whatever you want. God has set boundaries, as encapsulated in the Ten Commandments, not in order to confine us, but to protect us. Jesus summed up the commandments as loving God with all our heart, mind, soul and strength, and our neighbour as ourselves. Doing whatever you like without regard to God or your fellow humans will result in heartache and, ultimately, stress. Too much self-indulgence is as stressful as too much self-discipline. Again, you need to have balance.

## Balance of Exercise and Rest

In order to cope with stress, you have to keep your body healthy. And this means getting a balance of exercise and rest. Since there is a tendency nowadays to be sedentary, you need to be especially vigilant at ensuring that your body has sufficient exercise – and that you have a healthy diet. Physical exercise improves stamina, suppleness and strength, as well as helping you stay slim. Also, people who exercise regularly produce more endorphins, the body's natural morphine-like substances, in stressful situations. The best all-round activities are aerobics, gymnastics and swimming. But what is important is that you do something you enjoy, whether this is walking, jogging, dancing, or taking part in some kind of sport. However, exercise must be counterbalanced by frequent periods of physical rest, which means that you don't exercise crazily for weeks on end and then crash out and spend the next few days in bed. As discussed, rest

can involve taking time to just sit in the garden, read a book, listen to music, have a leisurely bath.... We need rest for the body, just as we need rest for the soul.

## Balance of Companionship and Solitude

In order to cope especially with encounter stress, you need to balance your need for people with your need for times of solitude. We were not meant to be alone; we were created as social beings. But in order to be sociable, you have to go where people are: church, evening classes, drama group, sports club.... With many activities you can combine your need to play and exercise with your need for company. However, if you have a job that involves constantly dealing with demanding or needy people, you must find time to get away by yourself, if possible during the working day, if only for a few minutes. At home, it is important that you do things together as a family, that you have times for just you and your partner, and that you have periods when you can be totally alone, doing whatever you want to do in your own time and your own way.

Getting the right balance can be difficult, especially if you were damaged emotionally in childhood and, as a result, are now struggling with low self-esteem, anger, guilt or fear. All these can get in the way, preventing you from changing attitudes and behaviours and so causing discouragement and a sense of futility and hopelessness; or, if you do succeed for a time, causing you to slip back into your old ways. For this reason, as well as learning some coping techniques and acquiring balance, you also have to return to your past, expose the root causes of stress, and find ways of dealing with them. It is only then that something new and healthy can emerge, making your life richer, fuller and calmer.

# 5

## GROWING BEYOND STRESS

### DEAL WITH PAST STRESSORS

#### Recall Past Hurts

The soul is eternal. There is no past, present or future. This is why, although we live in the context of time, you cannot cope with stress by blotting out or ignoring anything that has gone before. You have to remember the past. This means honestly facing up to it and admitting to yourself where parents, or significant others, may have failed – whether or not this was intentional. This is not in order to allocate blame, but to understand how you have been shaped by parental influences and predisposed to stress. It is only as you are able to face the truth that you can be free. You need to remember first, the facts of your childhood, and then the feelings that went with them.

The facts most associated with a tendency to stress usually revolve around emotional abuse, which includes being put down, condemned, disapproved of, or constantly criticised. (When there has been physical or sexual abuse, this is more likely to lead primarily to depression.) As discussed in Chapter 2, the emotional abuse may not have been obvious: it may have taken the form of backhanded compliments, lack of praise or encouragement, parents not being there to help with homework or being so caught up with their own agendas that you felt you had to make it alone. Or perhaps you had parents who were very intelligent or successful and you sensed that they also expected you to excel. Conversely, you might have been ashamed of your family and felt driven to rise above them. But perhaps the most damaging is having parents who failed to recognise your unique strengths and abilities and tried to push you into a mould of their own making.

As you think back over the facts of your childhood, incidents, looks, gestures or spoken words will come to mind, and

you will be able to start putting them together to form a pattern. You will then have a better idea of how you may be repeating the prototype and creating your own stress. At the same time, consider how you might have felt as you were growing up. Put yourself in a child's shoes so that you can identify with the child part of yourself and better understand yourself. Then reflect on how you are feeling now. You may, for instance, feel sadness, regret, anger or grief. It is important that you allow yourself to feel – to grieve, be angry, etc. – so that you can move beyond the feelings. When emotions are not allowed to surface, perhaps because of the fear of being overwhelmed by them, the hurts of the past remain.

### Allow Wounds to Heal

Whether wounds are physical or emotional, they have to be attended to, otherwise they will fester. And you begin by admitting to yourself that you have been hurt, and acknowledging the full extent of the injury. It will help if you can then find someone to talk to about your painful experiences; someone who will listen and understand, who won't give advice or tell you what to do, but will simply be there for you. Putting hurts into words is very releasing, especially if you are also able to safely give vent to the associated feelings. You can do this perhaps by allowing yourself to cry, or by articulating your anger. Expressing your long-buried memories, thoughts and feelings cleanses the wounds, allowing the edges to come together so that healing can take place.

The wounds must then be left alone. They cannot heal if you are continuing the patterns of childhood by hurting yourself. Therefore, you must get out of the habit of putting yourself down, telling yourself that you are stupid, ugly, or whatever. If you are having trouble with this, then ask God to show you the essentially good and beautiful person hidden inside, the person he created, values and loves. He can show you this in many different ways, perhaps through a partner, friend, church leader or counsellor. Wounds also cannot heal if you hold onto your anger, or re-contaminate them with false guilt and generalised fear.

When emotional wounds are cleaned and then left alone, the soul, just like the body, is able to heal itself. But you can assist the healing by nurturing this life-giving, creative part of the self, building it up so that it can more effectively and quickly bring about natural healing. This means giving yourself some tender, loving care, feeding your soul on beauty and truth, and allowing it space. It is also essential that you allow others to nurture you, through the provision of care and assistance and their unconditional acceptance of the essential you. But before people can get close enough to do this, you have to remove the defences.


## REMOVE OUTMODED DEFENCES

### Recognise the Defences

When you are under attack, the typical stress reaction prepares the body for fight or flight. But when attacks are frequent there is a natural propensity to build psychological defences to prevent the necessity of endlessly fighting the same battles or constantly running. The defences, then, serve a useful purpose during emotional warfare. The problem is, there is a tendency to keep on using them when the danger has passed, and then, rather than helping you survive, they prevent you from getting on with life.

A common defence mechanism is denial. Children who are consistently hurt by grown ups often cope by telling themselves that it isn't happening. Or they imagine that they are someone else, in another place, perhaps with different parents, so the bad things are happening to another child. Another defence mechanism involves the shutting down of feelings so that harsh words or physical blows no longer have any effect. A third type of defence is withdrawal: children cope with abuse, of whatever kind, by cutting themselves off from other people, living in a little world of their own. Or, they may use the defence of perfectionism, trying to be perfect, or kidding themselves that they are perfect; because when you don't have any faults you are loved and admired by everyone, and you never get hurt.

In later life, when the defences have become superfluous, they lead to self-induced stress. For instance, if you have developed the habit of denying reality, you will go through life unable to recognise potentially harmful people or situations, so you will keep on exposing yourself to danger. This in turn will necessitate an ongoing fight or flight response. Similarly, if you shut down your feelings you will be unable to recognise how other people or circumstances are affecting you, so you will not see the necessity for change. If you tend to withdraw, you will become increasingly isolated and lonely, and the false sense of being alone in a hostile world will make you want to hide away even more. At the same time, the build-up of anger will make you periodically want to come out fighting, venting your anger on whoever happens to be nearest. The need to be perfect is very stressful because of the constant drive to achieve the impossible, and the strain of keeping your true self hidden from the very people who want to get close to you and meet your emotional needs.

### Take down the Defences

When psychological defences are still used in peacetime, they keep you trapped in fortresses of your own making, preventing you from moving forward in life. And they keep others out. However, if you have been using defences – such as denial, shut-down, withdrawal or perfectionism – for a long time, you will need to remove them one bit at a time. If you expose yourself too much and too quickly you won't feel safe, so you will want to keep running back into your hiding place.

If your defence is denial, then you will need to work at facing up to the reality of any past hurts, whether they occurred in childhood or adult life, as well as your present existence. It is only as you are able to see people and things as they really are that you can do something about them. If you deny reality through excessive daydreaming, you will need to take control of your mind and start focusing on the world around you. There is, of course, a place for daydreaming. It relaxes the mind and is a form of stress management, as well as a source of creativity. But when daydreaming is used as a defence, to prevent you from seeing the truth, then it does not serve a useful function.

If you tend to shut down emotionally, you can reverse this trend by asking yourself, whenever you feel stressed, "What am I feeling?" You will then need to start identifying the various shades of feelings, and practice putting the right labels on them; labels such as abandonment, betrayal, loneliness, emptiness.... At the same time, allow yourself to express your feelings appropriately – at the right time and in the right place – through crying, having a grump about something, or whatever you find the most releasing. If you have a habit of telling yourself not to be silly, or to just pull yourself together and get on with it, then begin treating yourself with more compassion and understanding, reminding yourself that feelings that are not allowed expression stay inside and fester, making you more vulnerable to stress.

If your defence is to withdraw, then begin to remove this particularly isolating form of entrapment by starting to mix with other people. Go where people are: church, clubs, night school, etc. Find something that appeals to you and start making friends. If, as well as withdrawing, you tend to periodically break out in acts of aggression, then learn how to recognise and control anger. The book in this series, *Beyond Anger: Growing into calm*, will help you with this.

If you are a perfectionist, then you will need to work hard at getting the balance right: striving to do your best and realise your potential, but without making impossible demands upon yourself. This is a particularly difficult defence to remove because of the associated false belief that to be less than perfect means lowering your standards. But this is not the case. Being less than perfect means being human, and when you can allow yourself to be the same as everyone else, it makes life a lot easier – and a lot richer.

As your defences come down, you will find your world expanding. You will discover new facets of truth about yourself, meet new and more interesting people, and find new opportunities and challenges. You will also grow and develop emotionally so that, as you emerge from your walled fortress, you will be able to adapt and cope with the inevitable changes. However, in order to keep yourself from retreating behind your defences whenever you feel pressured or threatened, you will also need to continue working at recognising, and putting a stop to, those destructive patterns of behaviour that arise from having an unhealthy need for high drama, to be special, to be punished or be a rescuer. As you do this, you will become increasingly more aware of your normal, legitimate needs, and be able to meet them through the development of healthy and fulfilling relationships.

**Learn to Relate**

We all have needs, and in order to cope with stress it is important to acknowledge them and, as far as possible, fulfil them. This means, first of all, recognising that it is unrealistic to expect any one person or situation to meet all your emotional requirements. For example, you may have thought, if only I could meet the right partner, I will be happy. Or, if I could only have a child, I would have everything I ever wanted. But this is asking too much. A partner cannot meet your maternal needs, and children cannot meet your need for mental stimulation or adult company. And no one can meet those exaggerated needs that make you particularly prone to stress.

If you are now realising that you have a need for high drama, you can increase your new awareness by connecting this with those times when you weren't listened to or noticed as a child, and by disentangling the present from the past. This will make you freer to look at your current situation, to ask yourself if people are listening to you now, and if not, why not? Are you, for example, still throwing tantrums, being provocative, or antagonising people to make them aware of your existence? These methods of getting attention are destructive. They threaten people and make them threatening in return. Therefore, being able to acknowledge and understand your need for high drama will enable you to start looking at less stressful ways of fulfilling the basic human need for someone to listen and understand.

If you have a particular need to be special because of having been neglected, disregarded or devalued in childhood, then, likewise, recognising the link between your current behaviour and past hurts will begin the process of setting you free. And the more liberated you become, the more you will be able to realise your innate specialness and therefore lose the need to be the most successful, the cleverest or most talented, to have the biggest house or car, or to have suffered or endured more than anyone else. You will be able to get down off your pedestal and join the rest of the human race. And this will take a tremendous burden off yourself.

If you are becoming aware of a previously unconscious need to be punished, then you can start letting go of any false guilt by telling yourself, over and over, that you were not to blame for the way grown-ups treated you in childhood. You must also keep reminding yourself that you are not responsible for other people's general state of unhappiness – you are only responsible for your own thoughts, feelings and actions. The deeper this awareness goes, the more you will be able to stop punishing yourself and provoking others to punish you. You will be able to relate better and, without the constant threat of others' retaliatory anger, abuse or contempt, you will not have to live in a constant state of readiness for fight or flight.

If you have a deep-rooted need to be a rescuer, then recognising that you are vicariously meeting your own needs through caring for others will free you from this intolerable burden. This does not mean that you have to resign from a caring profession, or stop being concerned about everyone else. On the contrary. What it does mean is that you will be able to set boundaries so that others do not intrude on your own time and space. You will also be able to start allowing others to care for you, thereby increasing your reserves so that you can actually give more, without draining yourself in the process.

Whatever your particular unconscious need: to be a dramatist, a hero or heroine, a naughty child or a rescuer, you will at first have to be very vigilant at noticing your patterns of behaviour and the effect they have on others. You will also have to work continuously at linking your current behaviours with childhood needs and aims. But your efforts will pay off as you find yourself increasingly able to look at alternative, more healthy ways of getting your needs met; ways that do not induce stress but instead liberate you, so that you can become the person you really want to be.


## SET YOURSELF FREE

### Improve your Self-esteem

In order to realise your potential in all areas of life, it is essential that you have a healthy self-esteem. However, when this has been damaged in childhood, there is a tendency to continue the pattern by putting yourself down: telling yourself that you are stupid, ugly, or whatever. There is also a propensity to discount the positive and focus on the negative, attributing any achievements or successes to luck, and seeing failure as the result of your own inadequacy. These patterns lower self-esteem even further, making you more sensitive to others' perceived put-downs, and causing you to read into their comments, gestures and facial expressions things that are not actually there. There is then a continuing sense of threat, with a corresponding need for a safe, high wall to retreat behind.

The topic of self-esteem is wide ranging, and is discussed in depth in the book by this author, *Self-esteem: the Way of Humility*. Perhaps the main points to be noted here are, first, that we were meant to esteem ourselves. God made us essentially good, and he gave everyone gifts and talents that he intends us to use. Also, self-esteem is not the same as selfishness, and neither is it pride or conceit. Rather, it is a true recognition of our given worth and potential, and the ability to realistically assess our strengths as well as our weaknesses. When we truly esteem ourselves we are better able to relate, not just to other people but also to the entire created world. We therefore have a sense of connectedness as well as a sense of our own individuality.

Self-esteem is built on our sense of identity – who we are. And this is formed first and foremost by God, who created us to be loved and valued, and to have responsibility for the rest of the created world. We are also shaped by our socio-political and ecclesiastical history, our culture, our families and by our own beliefs, values, interests and goals. It follows, then, that the more you know about yourself and your environment, the firmer will

be your sense of identity, and the healthier and more stable will be your self-esteem.

In order to build self-esteem, it is necessary to enhance every aspect of the self: heart, mind, body, soul and spirit. This means that you have to work at forming positive relationships, developing and using your mental capacities, keeping your body fit and attractive, tapping into your creative ability, and learning to love and trust God. Healthy self-esteem can be summarised as the ability to live in harmony with yourself, other people, and your Creator.

### Discard your Anger

You cannot live in harmony with yourself or others if you are full of anger – repressed or otherwise. Therefore, you will need to start recognising this feeling in yourself, determine who you are angry with and, as the feelings comes to the surface, find an outlet for them. Since anger is a form of energy, it is especially helpful if you release it by doing something physical: pummel a pillow, run round the block, scrub a floor.... These are first-aid measures for discharging the excessive build-up of this very powerful emotion; they are not long-term methods. And the golden rule is that you do nothing that harms yourself, other people or property. When you have released the tension, you must then let the anger go. This will reduce your anger base level, making it far easier to deal with current stressors, especially those that create feelings of frustration or annoyance. Letting go is the essence of forgiveness.

Forgiveness is not the same as denying or minimising – "It wasn't all that bad!" Neither is it the same as excusing – "She couldn't help it." And it is not tolerating: you don't have to keep exposing yourself to the same hurt. Forgiveness is, in effect, letting go of the need for revenge or restitution. It is like writing off a bad debt, and although this is hurtful and there is naturally a sense of loss, once you have written it off you are free to get on with your life. It is important to remember, however, that forgiveness is a process. It doesn't happen all at once. And for there to be full forgiveness there has to be a full awareness of the wrong done to you. So if you find yourself getting angry with

70

someone all over again, it doesn't necessarily mean that you never forgave in the first place; it means that you now have to forgive at a deeper level.

When there is a refusal to forgive, legitimate anger gives way to bitterness and malice – and these destroy the self. You actually end up fighting yourself whilst also hating and wanting to run from yourself. This is because, unless you are entirely without conscience, you create in yourself feelings of guilt. And these feelings, if not recognised and acted upon, become confused with any residual false guilt.

**Reject False Guilt**

As noted in Chapter 2, children who have been abused are especially prone to false guilt. But children are not to blame for anything that adults may have done to them or made them feel. And they certainly have no reason to feel guilty for having been born, been the wrong sex, or for not living up to their parents' ideal. All this is false guilt because it is not connected with personal wrongdoing. And the only thing you can do with false guilt is to reject it.

However, false guilt may be working in you more subtly. For instance, you may not feel that you are to blame for anything, but still have a mother's voice inside you telling you that you can't sit down and have a break until you've made the beds; or a now absent father still telling you that you can't go out and have fun until you have finished a work project. These parental voices will prevent you from developing the balance in your life that is essential for coping with stress. This is why you have to get at the roots of the problem and banish the guilt. Only then will you be able to stop pressurising yourself and start discovering your interests, develop some hobbies, and do things just because they are fun, without constant fear of retribution.

**Eliminate Generalised Fear**

Fear is useful when it arouses you to danger, getting the adrenalin going so that you can fight or flee. So you should not attempt to banish fear entirely, but learn to differentiate between legitimate fear and the more vague, free-floating anxiety that is a legacy of abuse, rejection or constant criticism. You can begin to do this by learning to recognise specific examples of transferred fear. For instance, if you feel anxious around people in positions of authority, or have a constant vague feeling that you will be punished if you put a foot wrong, then this fear may have originated with an authoritarian father and, during childhood, been transferred onto all male relatives or teachers. In time the fear will have been generalised to all authority figures, including God.

It is also possible to transfer fear onto objects or places. Often the connection is obvious. For example, claustrophobia may have arisen because of a traumatic incident occurring in an enclosed place. But sometimes this kind of generalised fear is not so easy to identify. This is because there is a psychological tendency to replace a fear that cannot be acknowledged with a more acceptable one. If you struggle with fear, then the book in this series, *Beyond Fear: Growing into faith*, will help you also deal with this very common problem.

When you have identified the true source of your fear, you will then need to mentally put it where it belongs. As you do this, the fear you have transferred onto other people or places will lessen, and you will be able to start seeing them as they really are. You will discover, for example, that not all men are like an abusive father, nor all women like a domineering mother, so you will feel progressively safer. You will find that, in spite of the very real dangers that exist in today's world, it is still full of good, honest people whom you can trust and rely on. And, you will be able to trust God in a new way, and experience the peace that exists in him.

**Develop an inner peace**
Because we live in a stressful society, now perhaps more than at any other time in history, we need to be aware of stress and its effects on the mind and body, to learn how to manage it and grow beyond it. This does not mean that you will never again know fear or unrest; it means that you can learn to experience an inner peace that is not dependent on external circumstances – as did Moses, Rebekah and Nehemiah. This serenity comes, in part,

from the release that is experienced when you shed any baggage from the past, from a deepening knowledge of yourself, and from an increasing ability to come aside from the world, to find rest and relaxation in the midst of turmoil. It comes also from an awareness and experience of the essential goodness of human beings, including yourself.

The more you become aware of your own inherent value, the more you will sense the existence of a place of safety deep within your own psyche. And this in turn will enable you to grow, unchecked and without fear, into the person you want to be. But in order to find this place of safety you have to listen to yourself; to what your body, heart and mind are telling you. You also have to be yourself, and go with the flow, instead of fighting against your own instincts and judgements. It is also important that you learn to stop and listen to the voice and rhythm of the universe so that you can live in harmony with all of created life. Above all, you need to listen to the divinity within: the still, small voice of God that speaks to everyone who has ears to hear, telling us that there is more to this life than a constant, restless urge to get ahead; a voice that offers rest to the weary and heavy-laden. [7] Only then can you grow beyond stress into a state of perfect serenity.

# Endnotes

1     Luke 10. 41-42
2     Exodus 14.14
3     Exodus 18.17-18
4     Nehemiah 4.2
5     Nehemiah 4.3
6     Philippians 4.8
7     Matthew 11.28-30

# Silvertree Grobooks

## Jennifer Minney

**Beyond depression: Growing into light**
ISBN: 0-9538446-3-3

**Beyond fear: Growing into faith**
ISBN: 0-9538446-5-X

**Beyond stress: Growing into serenity**
ISBN: 0-9538446-4-1

Using Bible characters as case studies, each book discusses signs and symptoms, current triggers and deep-rooted causes, and provides guidelines for overcoming the immediate effects. The emotional difficulties are also viewed in the context of the entire person, and the reader is helped to find healing from past traumas and begin changing destructive patterns of thinking and behaviour; to move beyond the problem towards spiritual and psychological wholeness.

**All titles £3.50**

**Coming soon:**

**Beyond anger: Growing into calm**
**Beyond marital discord: Growing into love**
**Beyond parenting chaos: Growing into harmony**

# Also by Jennifer Minney

## Self-esteem: The way of humility

This thoughtful book promotes the development of self-esteem on the basis of one's identity in God, through creation and redemption. This foundation, it explains, is essential for creating a respect for self that is humble and grateful, and that leads to a more responsible and effective stewardship of one's gifts and abilities.

The author, a counsellor with a BA (Hons) in Psychology, and more than twenty years experience of helping people with low self-esteem, draws also on her Bible college, nursing and midwifery training to explore and discuss five aspects of the self: body, soul, spirit, heart and mind. With each, there is a survey of common misconceptions and problems, with guidelines for overcoming them.

**£5.95**                                    **ISBN: 0-9538446-2-5**

## Will Jesus kick my ball back?

The amazing story of an adoption that should have been impossible, of cerebral palsy, and a child whose avid curiosity and irrepressible giggles have made him a joy to many.

It is also the story of the author's spiritual and psychological journey, from a background of abuse and rejection, through years of infertility, to a place of trust in God's goodness, even when his long-promised child turns out to be severely brain-damaged. It is a story of learning to open up to God's love and experiencing him, no longer as rigid and punitive, but as a loving, approachable Father with whom it is safe to be oneself, to be child-like — to play.

The two stories blend as mother and child grow together, developing their full potential as she learns to love herself and a child whom a neurologist had written off.

This book has had a profound impact on those who have read it, provoking laughter, producing tears, challenging, uplifting and enriching the soul. It is a book that is hard to put down.

**£6.95**                                    **ISBN: 0-9538446-0-9**

All Silvertree titles are available from bookshops or can be purchased (postage free in UK) direct from:

**Silvertree Publishing**
**PO Box 2768**
**Yeovil**
**Somerset  BA22 8XZ**

## Become a Silvertree Book Agent

If you found this book helpful, why not become a Silvertree Book Agent, and so benefit others whilst also earning money for yourself, your church, or your favourite charity?

For full details, send an s.a.e. to the above address.